THE BROCKHAMPTON LIBRARY

book of
Herbs

BROCKHAMPTON PRESS
LONDON

Introduction

Although the following list is by no means an exhaustive one, it will provide an introduction to many of the best-known and loved herbs grown in this country. When trying out herbal remedies, bear in mind that any serious or persistent condition should always be treated by a qualified medical practitioner. As some people may be allergic to certain herbs it is always advisable to consult a qualified herbalist for advice on dosage or strength before taking any herbal preparations.

Agrimony *Agrimonia eupatoria*

Description
This attractive perennial grows abundantly by
roadsides and on riverbanks. It has a slender stem,
which can reach a height of two to three feet, and
long, thin, saw-edged leaves. In summer, tiny
blossoms form a spike along the top of the stalk.
These yellow, star-shaped flowers have a delicate
apricot scent.

Origins
Agrimony is native to the British Isles and was held in
high regard during the Middle Ages for the tonic brew
made from its leaves. A concoction of the roots and
leaves was used in the 17th century for easing kidney
problems.

Cultivation
Collect seeds from the dried stalk towards the end of the
year and plant them in the spring in ordinary dry soil.
Agrimony prefers full sun, although it will tolerate some
shade. To speed up propagation, divide the roots early
in the spring and set the segments about 20 cms apart.

Culinary Uses
Agrimony is not used in cooking.

Other Uses
Agrimony is of great value in the treatment of
persistent dry coughs, where its effect is gently

sedative. Some forms of rheumatism are also said to respond well to its action, and it has long been esteemed as a liver tonic. Both flowers and leaves retain their refreshing, fruity aroma when dried and are popular pot-pourri ingredients. The flowers can also be gathered late in the growing season and used as a dye yielding a yellow hue.

Angelica *Angelica archangelica*

Description
Angelica stems are stout, hollow, fluted and often grow to over 1½ metres in height. The leaves are bright green with a serrated edge and composed of numerous small leaflets, usually divided into groups of three. The flowers, which appear in July, are tiny and yellowish, grouped into large umbels. The whole plant has a sweet scent.

Origins
Some botanists believe angelica to be a native of Syria, from whence it spread to cooler countries where it has become naturalized. It is occasionally found growing wild in Scotland, but seems to prefer even cooler climes such as Lapland and Iceland.

Cultivation
Angelica is a biennial plant and should be grown in ordinary, deep, moist loam in a shady position, preferably near running water. Seeds should be sown in late summer in their final position then thinned out to 18 cms apart once they have germinated. If

prevented from flowering, the plants will live for a few years, but left to their own devices should self-seed and provide continuous new plants from year to year.

Culinary Uses

The stems and seed are used in confectionery and flavouring and also in the preparation of liqueurs. The young stems are frequently candied and used as cake decorations, and can also be used as flavouring for jellies and jams. The roots and stems may also be cooked as a vegetable.

Other Uses

An infusion of angelica is considered to be a good herbal remedy for colds, coughs, wind, colic and rheumatism, although it should be avoided by diabetes sufferers. Angelica tea relieves stress and tension, especially when taken late at night, and a bag of angelica leaves immersed in the bath will provide a relaxing hot soak.

Anise *Pimpinella anisum*

Description

Anise is a dainty, white-flowered umbelliferous annual, about 40 cms in height with secondary feather-like leaflets of bright green. The true leaves are finely toothed. When in bloom, the plants attain a height of about 60 cm.

Origins

Anise is a native of Egypt, Greece, Crete and Asia and was cultivated by the ancient Egyptians. It is one of the best-known digestive herbs and in Roman times the seeds were chewed after large meals.

Cultivation
Sow the seed early in April in dry, light soil on a warm, sunny border where the plants are to remain. When they come up, thin them and keep them free from weeds. Allow 30 cms each way. Alternatively, sow the seeds in pots indoors and transplant outdoors in May.

Culinary Uses
Anise has a strong flavour similar to liquorice. Throughout the summer, the leaves can be used to add flavour to green salads, and will also enhance fruit salads. The seeds are wonderful in bread, cakes, biscuits and fruit pies.

Other Uses
Anise is used in cough mixtures as an expectorant, and is also available in lozenge form to soothe sore throats. It also has a beneficial effect on the digestive tract, and is often given for colic, hiccups and flatulence. The seeds and the oil are both used in preparations to sweeten the breath and aid digestion.

Basil *Ocimum basilicum*

Description
Sweet basil has large shiny leaves that grow in pairs opposite each other and whorls of white or mauve-tinged flowers. It can grow to around 60 cms high.

Origins
Basil was originally a native of India but grows in most areas of Europe.

Cultivation
In temperate countries such as ours, basil needs to be grown every year from seed, preferably indoors. Once seedlings have been hardened off (i.e. placed outdoors daily for increasing periods of time) and after all risk of frost has passed, they may be planted outdoors in a sunny, sheltered site. Soil needs to be fairly light, rich and free-draining. Alternatively, grow in pots on a sunny kitchen windowsill for a ready supply.

Culinary Uses
Basil is one of the most popular culinary herbs and is the main ingredient of Italian pesto sauce. It has a particular affinity for eggs, pasta, tomatoes and mushrooms and evokes a wonderful Mediterranean flavour. The fresh leaves brighten up green salads and impart a warmth to salad dressings.

Other Uses
Though generally employed as a flavouring agent, basil has been used occasionally for mild nervous disorders and in the treatment of rheumatic pains. The dried leaves were traditionally used in the form of snuff to alleviate headaches. An infusion of basil is said to be useful in the treatment of digestive disturbances such as constipation and nausea.

Bay *Laurus nobilis*

Description

Bay (or laurel, as it is sometimes known) is a small tree, which can reach a height of 7 metres in this country and as much as 18 metres in warmer climes. The smooth bark may be olive-green or of a reddish blue. The luxurious, evergreen leaves are alternate and 8–10 cms long. The small, yellow flowers grow in small clusters.

Origins

The bay tree is native to the shores of the Mediterranean, and has been cultivated in this country since the 16th century. Since ancient times the bay has symbolized both bravery and learning, and the modern term 'bachelor' (awarded for degrees) is probably derived from 'baccalaureus', or laurel-berry.

Cultivation

Bay trees can be difficult to grow in this country and should be planted in ordinary garden soil in a sunny location. They will rarely survive the winter outdoors and are therefore best planted in large containers so that they can be brought indoors.

Culinary Uses

Bay has a marvellous flavour that has long been popular in cookery—it is one of the main ingredients of *bouquet-garni,* a small parcel of herbs wrapped in muslin which is used to flavour a multitude of soups and stews.

Other Uses

Bay is rarely used nowadays either medicinally or in cosmetic preparations, but historically it was used to cure colic, amenorrhoea and even hysteria.

Bergamot *Monarda didyma*

Description

Bergamot has become a garden favourite with its wonderful aroma and its showy scarlet flowers and pale green leaflets tinged with red. Its square, hard and grooved stems grow to a height of about 60 cms.

Origins

Bergamot was originally a native of North America, where the native Oswego Indians made a soothing tea from its flowers and leaves.

Cultivation

Bergamot prefers a light, moist soil in an area that is exposed to morning sun only. It should be propagated by dividing its creeping roots or taking cuttings or slips. The plant should be removed to a different position in the garden every 2–3 years.

Culinary Uses

The fresh leaves and flowers make a refreshing and relaxing tea, and also add flavour and colour to fruit jellies, juices and punch. Try also adding some leaves to a late-night cup of hot milk for a soothing, sedative effect. Leaves and flowers added to an otherwise dull salad will add flavour and interest.

Other Uses
Although bergamot teas have a soothing, relaxing effect, it is not much used as a medicinal herb.

Borage *Borago officinalis*

Description
Borage is rough to touch with white, stiff, prickly hairs. It grows to about 45 cms in height and has bright blue star-shaped flowers that sport prominent black anthers that form a cone in the centre.

Origins
Borage is thought to have come originally from southern India, but is now naturalized in most parts of Europe. The Romans knew borage as a herb that would banish sadness when drunk in wine.

Cultivation
Borage has a long tap root that renders it unsuitable for containers. However, it grows well in a light, sandy soil in a sunny position. It should be grown from seed as it does not tolerate transplantation well. The seeds germinate quickly and the plant will attain its full height in 5 or 6 weeks. Left alone, borage seeds freely and will come up year after year in the same place.

Culinary Uses
The leaves have a flavour not unlike that of cucumber and are often chopped and used in salads or soups. Another popular use is as a tea, either hot or iced with lemon and sugar added.

Other Uses
The tea has been traditionally used to ease fevers and lung complaints. It is also thought to have diuretic and anti-depressant effects.

Bugle *Ajuga reptans*

Description
Bugle is a creeping perennial with a squarish stem that is topped in the spring and summer by whorls of little blue flowers. The leaves are oval and shiny and grow outwards in clusters through a network of runners. Its foliage can range in colour from deep green to various shades of reddish-purple, depending on the season.

Origins
Bugle has grown in all parts of Europe for hundreds of years. In the 13th century in England it is on record as having been known as 'thunder and lightning', in reference to the brightness of its flowers and dark shine of its leaves. In German folklore it is held that to pick bugle flowers and bring them indoors will cause fire.

Cultivation
Bugle can flourish in a wide range of conditions, in sun or shade, moist or dry soil. Set young nursery plants 20 to 25 cms apart. The new young plants that appear at the ends of runners can easily be cut free for transplanting in the spring or autumn.

Culinary Uses

Other than being a good digestive and having a sedative effect on an upset stomach, bugle has no culinary use.

Other Uses

Bugle is popular among gardeners because it spreads so thickly that it stops the growth of weeds. In the past the root of the plant has been used as a black dye for woollens. It has also been used in the past in ointments for the treatment of ulcers, wounds and bruises. Today it is popular as a tea with general restorative properties.

Camomile *Chamaemelum nobile*

Description

A low-growing plant with a fragrant, daisy-like flower and feathery, thread-like leaves. There are various different forms of camomile, but 'true' camomile can be recognised by petals which turn back to expose the receptacle.

Origins

True camomile is native to Britain, but a number of species also grow in Europe and temperate regions of Asia and Africa.

Cultivation

Camomile is easily grown from seed in a sunny, well-drained position. The tiny seeds are best mixed with sand and sown in early spring. The seeds should

be watered until leaves appear and then thinned to
15 cms apart. Bear in mind that only the flowers are of
use and therefore only a relatively large planting will
be worthwhile.

Culinary Uses

Camomile has quite a bitter taste and is not often used
in cookery.It is very popular, however, as a herbal tea.
It is also used to flavour the Spanish sherry,
Manzanilla.

Other Uses

Camomile is widely used in infusion for its marvellous
calming, sedative effects. Sometimes combined with
ginger, camomile infusion provides a remedy for
indigestion and other digestive disturbances such as
colic, heartburn and constipation. It is also used to
cure occasional headaches. In addition to infusion,
camomile flowers are also extensively used by
themselves, or combined with poppy-heads as a
poultice and fomentation for external swelling,
inflammatory pain (such as that caused by
abscesses) and neuralgia. Altogether a most useful
medicinal herb.

Caraway *Carum carvi*

Description

Caraway is a biennial plant with smooth, furrowed stems,
growing 45 to 60 cms high, bearing feathery, finely cut
leaves and large umbels of white flowers that blossom in

June. The leaves emit a pleasant, aromatic flavour when bruised and also have a pleasant taste.

Origins

The plant is distributed throughout the central and northern parts of Europe and Asia, and is naturalized in some parts of this country, although it is generally regarded as a garden escape. Although the plant is mainly grown for its seeds, the roots are also edible and similar to parsnips. In fact, Roman armies are reputed to have incorporated caraway roots in a nourishing bread. The name is derived from *karaways*, an old Arabic word for seed. In ancient Greece, Dioscorides recommended that the essential oil of the plant be taken by those poor women afflicted with unfashionably pale skins!

Cultivation

Caraway does best when sown in late summer or early autumn in its final position, which should ideally be in well-drained soil and full sun. The seed will germinate quickly and seedlings should be thinned to a distance of 20 cms apart. An autumn-grown crop should produce seeds the following summer.

Culinary Uses

The seeds have long been used in bread and cake-making, and in Germany, cheese, cabbage, soups and stews have long been flavoured with caraway. The flavour goes well with pork and liver, and also adds interest to vegetables such as potato and cauliflower.

Other Uses
Caraway is mainly a culinary herb, but was widely used at one time as a cure for dyspepsia. Nowadays the oil is mainly used in combination with other medicines as a flavouring.

Chervil *Anthriscus cerefolium*

Description
Chervil is a wiry, fern-like biannual rising to a height of between 30 and 60 cms. It has large umbels of tiny white flowers and leaves that have a scent and flavour not unlike parsley but with a hint of anise.

Origins
Chervil most probably originated from south-east Europe and western Asia but is now widely grown and naturalized elsewhere. Although there seems to be little in the way of legend or history surrounding chervil, it has been much valued as a culinary herb since the Middle Ages.

Cultivation
As a result of rapid germination, it is possible to make several sowings of seeds throughout the year, thus ensuring a more or less constant supply of chervil. The seeds require a well-drained soil and partial shade. Seedlings require to be thinned to a distance of 15 cms apart. Chervil also grows happily in window boxes and other containers.

Culinary Uses

The leaves of the plant make a delicious soup, and should be added to butter sauces as an accompaniment to vegetables, and also to green salads. Chervil also blends well with cheese and egg dishes, and makes a tasty garnish for pork chops and beef steaks, as well as carrots, peas and tomatoes.

Other Uses

Although not often used medicinally, chervil has long been credited with blood-cleansing properties and is recommended as a skin tonic and cleanser.

Chicory *Cichorium intybus*

Description

Chicory is a perennial that can grow up to 1½ metres tall if left unhindered. It produces light blue, white or pink daisy-like flowers along its lanky stem. These blossoms open and close like clockwork, morning and evening.

Origins

Chicory features strongly in European folklore and has always been highly regarded on the Continent for its thick tap roots, which are dried, roasted and ground and added to coffee. This coffee and chicory mixture has been imported into Britain for more than a century.

Cultivation

Chicory needs full sun and will grow in almost any soil. Plant the seeds in early summer, covering thinly with soil, and thin to about 30 cms apart when the first leaves appear. Chicory does not flower the first year but blossoms will appear during succeeding years.

Culinary Uses

The Romans used chicory in their salads, but the leaves are bitter and unpalatable and today it is more commonly used as fodder for livestock. There are special strains of chicory, however, that are grown as gourmet vegetables. These are known as witloof chicory and Belgian endives, and they are cultivated by transplanting the chicory root in late autumn to a deep box of sand, which should then be kept moist in a cool, dark place. In 3 or 4 weeks a tightly furled bud of creamy-white foliage will sprout from the top of the root; this may be cooked whole or separated for use in a salad.

Other Uses

Chicory has no special place in the modern herbal, although at one time in England water distilled from the flowers that opened and closed with the sun was thought to cure jaundice, rheumatism, gout and failing eyesight.

Chive *Allium schoenoprasum*

Description

Chive is a hardy perennial with bulbs that grow very close together in clusters and long, cylindrical leaves that taper to a point. The flowerheads are round and mauve in colour, but are usually nipped off as this appears to preserve the flavour of the leaves.

Origins

Chive is said to be a native of Britain, but is rarely found growing wild here. It is, however, found growing wild throughout large areas of Europe, although little is known of its history.

Cultivation

The chive will grow in any garden soil. It can be raised from seed, but is usually propagated by dividing the clumps in spring or early autumn. Plant clumps of 6 or so tiny bulbs at a distance of 25 to 30 cms apart.

Culinary Uses

The chive is a member of the onion family, with a similar flavour, and is a welcome addition to salads when finely chopped. Chives are also excellent in savoury omelettes, and may be chopped and boiled with potatoes that are to be mashed, or chopped fresh and sprinkled, just before serving, on mashed potatoes. They may also be put into soup, finely chopped, and are a welcome improvement to sausages, croquettes, etc, as well as an excellent addition to beefsteak puddings and pies.

Comfrey *Symphytum officinale*

Description

Comfrey can grow up to a metre in height and has very large coarse leaves of about 25 cms in length.

The leaves are covered with rough hairs that cause itching when touched. The flowers are creamy yellow or purplish blue and droop in paired clusters.

Origins
Comfrey is a native of Europe and temperate Asia. It is now common throughout England on the banks of rivers and ditches and other watery places.

Cultivation
Although it prefers a damp and shady situation, comfrey will grow in almost any soil. It is not really suited to container growing because of its large roots. It can be grown from seed or propagated by root division in the spring.

Culinary Uses
Fresh comfrey leaves can be treated like spinach, although they will be enhanced by a white sauce and a grated cheese topping. The chopped leaves can be added to a green salad or dipped in batter and deep-fried as fritters. Note, however, that only the young leaves should be used in cooking.

Other Uses
Comfrey was traditionally popular for bronchial complaints, and also as a gentle remedy in cases of diarrhoea and dysentery. The root is more effective than the leaves, although the leaves are judged to be valuable in compresses and poultices for the treatment of bruising, swelling and rheumatic pain.

Coriander *Coriandrum sativum*

Description

Coriander is an annual plant with erect stems, 30 to 60 cms high, with branched, fern-like leaves. The flowers are pale mauve and are arranged in short stalked umbels. After flowering, the seeds can be seen in symmetrical clusters, which fall as soon as they are ripe. The whole plant emits a rather unpleasant smell until the seeds are ripe, and for this reason it is best grown outdoors.

Origins

Coriander is thought to be native to the southern European countries and the Middle and Far East, and has been mentioned in the Bible, in ancient Sanskrit writings and in Roman documents. The seeds were credited with the power of conferring immortality in an ancient Chinese belief.

Cultivation

Coriander prefers a warm, dry light soil and a sunny situation. The seeds should be sown in April in mild dry weather, in shallow drills about 2 cms deep and 20 cms apart. As the seeds begin to ripen in August, the plant's disagreeable aroma gives way to a much more pleasant fragrance, and it is at this point that the plant should be harvested.

Culinary Uses

The fruit (or seed) is the most often used part of the plant, although the leaves are increasingly being used

in soups and salads and to garnish Indian dishes. The
seeds are frequently to be found in their ground state
as an ingredient of a multitude of Indian dishes and
also as a principal ingredient of commercially
prepared curry powders. The seeds will enhance
many vegetables when sprinkled directly onto them
during cookery, and savoury biscuits, breads and
cakes will be transformed by the addition of the
ground seeds.

Other Uses
Coriander is not often used as a medicinal herb,
although coriander water was traditionally much
favoured as colic relief. It was once used a great deal
to flavour unpleasant-tasting medicines (particularly
laxatives) but has largely been replaced by synthetic
flavourings.

Cumin *Cuminum cyminum*

Description
Cumin is an annual plant not dissimilar in appearance
to fennel, although it rarely reaches more than 30 cms
in height. The flowers are rose-coloured and appear in
umbels in June and July. The plant is grown for its
seed only, and these are oblong in shape and about
one centimetre long.

Origins
Cumin probably came from Egypt originally, but
from early times was cultivated in India, China and

countries bordering the Mediterranean. In the Middle Ages it was the commonest spice of European growth, popular in cookery and for its medicinal actions.

Cultivation

Although we import almost all our seeds from the Mediterranean countries, it is perfectly feasible to grow cumin in this country—in fact, it grows as far north as Norway. It is probably easier to start the seeds off in small pots indoors and to transplant them when established to a warm border in a sheltered site at a distance of 15 cms apart. When the seeds have ripened, the whole plant should be cut down and the drying process completed outdoors.

Culinary Uses

With the huge revival in interest in Eastern cookery over the last 30 years or so, cumin has enjoyed an enormous comeback. As well as featuring in a myriad of Indian and Oriental recipes, it has also become popular for flavouring traditional British vegetables, soups and stews, as well as breads, biscuits, chutneys and pickles.

Other Uses

Cumin is not often used as a medicinal herb these days, although its popularity in cooking may owe something to its excellent properties as a digestive stimulant and antispasmodic.

Dill *Anethum graveolens*

Description

Dill is a hardy annual that grows to 60 to 75 cms in height and is very like fennel, with feathery leaves on sheathing stalks. Unlike fennel, however, it seldom has more than one stalk. The flowers are tiny, yellow and appear on flat umbels and go on to produce great quantities of the flat fruits or seeds. The whole plant is aromatic, particularly the seeds, which are very pungent and bitter in taste.

Origins

Records of dill being used in cookery have been found dating back to early Egyptian times, and it seems that the plant originates from nearby south-west Asia. It grows wild in Spain, Portugal and Italy, but is rarely found in its wild state in northern Europe. As a drug, dill has been used since the earliest times and is referred to in the gospel of St Matthew.

Cultivation

Dill is a normally a very easy herb to grow, but it should not be planted in the same spot year after year as it is very exhaustive of soil fertility. It is advisable to sow the seeds in their final position, preferably in full sun and rich soil. Thin the seedlings to a distance of 30 cms apart. When the flowerheads have faded to brown, the seeds will have ripened, and the whole plant should be cut and brought indoors for drying.

Culinary Uses

Young dill leaves are used for flavouring soups, sauces, salads, cream-cheese sandwich spreads and fish dishes. Dill vinegar is a popular household condiment made by soaking the seeds in vinegar for a few days. Perhaps the most popular way of using dill seeds is in pickling cucumbers.

Other Uses

Dill is particularly good at relieving stomach discomfort, such as colic and indigestion, and the seeds can be boiled in a tea that will soothe away insomnia or hiccups.

Elder *Sambucus nigra*

Description

The elder is a hardy deciduous shrub with masses of flat-topped fragrant flowers followed by large dropping bunches of purplish-black berries.

Origins

Native to Britain.

Cultivation

The elder prefers a moist soil and a sunny situation. Although it is possible to grow outdoors from seed, it is easier to obtain cuttings from leafless shoots in the autumn and propagate in this way. Elderflowers are unsuitable for container growing. However, the flowers and berries are freely available in hedgerows.

Culinary Uses

Elderflowers have long been popular with home wine-makers, producing a wine not dissimilar to that obtained from the Muscatel grape. The flowers can also be used in a refreshing water ice and in cordials. Elderflower pancakes go well with gooseberry purée, whilst the flowers lend an extra fragrance to fruit pies and fritters. The berries are also popular in wine-making, and combine well with crab-apples in jams and jellies. They also provide a welcome change from currants in many desserts, fruit pies and tarts.

Other Uses

Elderberry syrup has an extremely soothing effect on coughs and upper respiratory tract infections. Tea made from the dried berries is said to provide relief from diarrhoea and colic.

Fennel *Foeniculum vulgare*

Description

Fennel is a beautiful hardy perennial shrub growing to a height of 1–1½ metres. It has feathery segmented leaves and bright golden flowers that bloom in large, flat umbels in July and August. The seeds are oval in shape and should be dried before use.

Origins

Fennel is indigenous to the shores of the Mediterranean, but it grows wild in many parts of Europe. The name *Foeniculum*, which was given by the Romans, comes from the Latin word meaning 'hay'—although it is hard to see the resemblance! Fennel was well known to the Ancient Greeks and the Romans for its aromatic shoots and edible roots. Pliny, in fact, credited it with no fewer than 22 separate medicinal properties. In medieval times, it was hung over doorways on Midsummer's Eve to ward off evil spirits.

Cultivation

Fennel will thrive almost anywhere and is easily propagated by sowing the seeds in ordinary soil early in April, in a sunny site. Seedlings should be thinned to 30 cms apart. To avoid the plant freely seeding itself each year, the flowerheads should be removed as they begin to fade.

Culinary Uses

Fennel has a flavour that seems to go particularly well with fish, and a few of the leaves or seeds will impart an excellent flavour to water for poaching or boiling fish. The leaves can also be chopped and used in sauces for fish. Alternatively, try adding freshly chopped fennel leaves to your salads or to buttered new potatoes.

Other Uses

Fennel has similar medicinal properties to those of anise and dill water. It seems to exert a soothing effect on digestive disturbances. It is a traditional favourite as a gripe water for infantile colic. Tired eyes will often be revived by the application of a fennel infusion.

Fennel tea is also credited with having a diuretic and mildly laxative action and is said to relieve cramps.

Garlic *Allium sativum*

Description
Garlic leaves are long, narrow and flat, like grass. The bulb, which is the only part used, consists of numerous bulblets, known as cloves, held together in a white skin. The flowers are whitish and grouped together to form a larger globular head in an enclosing leaf.

Origins
It is hard to trace the origins of garlic as it has been so widely used since early times. There is evidence that Ancient Egyptian labourers building the Pyramids used garlic in cookery, whilst Roman soldiers ate garlic for sustenance on long campaigns.

Cultivation
Garlic cloves grow best in rich, moist, sandy soil in full sun. They should be planted at a distance of 15 cms from each other and require regular watering throughout spring and summer. In cold areas, they should be planted in early spring, but in milder climes they can be planted in the autumn to produce a crop early in the following summer.

Culinary Uses
Garlic has a multitude of culinary uses in a variety of dishes. In this country, it has only been popular in

recent years, the flavour having been considered too strong for delicate British palates. However, with the rise in popularity of world cookery, the versatility of garlic has been realized.

Other Uses

Only now has medical science begun to confirm the value of garlic, known to herbalists for centuries. It has long been recognized as an antiseptic and was used to treat wounds in the First World War. It has also been used to treat asthma, hoarseness, coughs and rheumatism. Used in cookery, garlic is said to aid digestion and help ensure a healthy stomach lining, and for this purpose the essential oil can be taken in tablet form. Recent research has indicated that garlic may be responsible for reducing harmful fat deposit in the arteries, thus reducing the risk of circulatory problems.

Horseradish *Armoracia rusticana*

Description

The leaf stalks of the horseradish plant spring directly from the ground and grow to a height of 60–90 cms. The leaves themselves are large and floppy with toothed margins. The flowers are white and borne on single stems in airy sprays, but the plant does not always flower every season. The roots, which are the only parts used, are white and cylindrical and constitute a rich source of vitamin C.

Origins
The origin of the plant is uncertain, although it is most likely to have been from eastern Europe.

Cultivation
Horseradish roots need a finely filled soil rich in nutrients if they are to survive. The easiest method is to plant root cuttings of around 20 cms in length and 1 cm in width with any side root removed. With a dibber, make holes about 30 cms in depth and drop the root cuttings in. Cover them over with soil in a site that is sunny and open. The crop will need to be replaced every few years, otherwise it tends to deteriorate.

Culinary Uses
Horseradish sauce is the most popular accompaniment to the traditional English roast beef, although it was used by the Germans and Danes long before the English. It is also a stimulating addition to coleslaw and chutneys. It can also be mixed with other ingredients, such as cream cheese, to make a tasty sandwich spread.

Other Uses
When taken with rich meat or oily fish, horseradish acts as a stimulant to the digestive system. It has a strong diuretic action, and was used traditionally by herbalists to treat kidney stones and to treat scurvy because of its high vitamin C content. It is still popular with herbalists as a poultice for chilblains and aching joints and muscles.

Hyssop *Hyssopus officinalis*

Description

Hyssop is a bushy evergreen herb that grows to about 60 cm in height. It has a square stem, linear leaves and flowers arranged in whorls of about 10–15. There are three varieties, known by their blue, red and white flowers.

Origins

Hyssop is a native of southern Europe and the Middle East. In early times, it was used as a meat preservative and as a cleansing herb for medicinal purposes.

Cultivation

Hyssop will grow well from seeds planted in April in a shady situation. When large enough, the young plants should be transplanted to a warm aspect in light, rather dry soil at a distance of 30 cm apart. The plants should be pruned occasionally but otherwise require little attention. Hyssop can also be propagated from cuttings, and will grow happily in a container.

Culinary Uses

Hyssop leaves possess a light minty tang that adds interest to green salads and vegetable soups, and also enhances meat dishes such as lamb stew or rabbit. It also goes well with fruit, being a traditional addition to cranberries, stewed fruits and fruit tarts and pies, as well as a variety of fruit drinks.

Other Uses

Hyssop has long been favoured by herbalists for its

healing powers. In particular, hyssop tea is said to have a strong expectorant effect and is therefore useful in the treatment of colds and respiratory disorders. It is also said to soothe upset stomachs, and an infusion of the leaves was traditionally used in America to relieve muscular rheumatism.

Lavender *Lavandula vera*

Description
There are several different species of lavender, but the best known in this country is the one known as English lavender (*Lavendula vera*), which also possesses the best scent. Lavender is a perennial shrub with narrow grey leaves that grow to a height of about 60–90 cms. In late spring or early summer the beautiful bluish-violet flowers appear in whorls or rings of 6–10 on the thin stems that rise above the newest shoots.

Origins
Lavender is indigenous to mountainous regions of countries bordering the western half of the Mediterranean, but it has been grown very successfully for centuries in this country. In Elizabethan times lavender oil was rubbed into oak furniture to give a high gloss finish.

Cultivation
Lavender grows best on light, sandy or gravelly soil in an open, sunny position, but it needs some protection from strong winds and frost. Lavender

may be grown from seed in April, but speedier results will be obtained if the crop is grown from cuttings or root division. Cuttings with a heel should be planted in a box of sand in early summer and transplanted to their final position the following spring. They should be pruned after flowering to maintain a neat appearance.

Culinary Uses
In Tudor times, lavender was widely used in cookery, but today its principal use is in perfumery.

Other Uses
Herbalists have traditionally used lavender for a multitude of ailments. It is gentle enough to use directly on the skin and is popular in the treatment of burns, wounds and skin conditions. One of its most popular applications was as an ingredient in furniture polish because of its insect-repellent properties. In an embrocation, lavender oil relieves muscular stiffness, and cold compresses containing a few drops of the oil are said to relieve headaches.

Lemon balm *Melissa officinalis*

Description
Lemon balm is a fragrant, lemon-scented perennial plant that grows to a height of 30–60 cms. It has white or yellowish flowers that grow in loose, small bunches from the axils of the leaves from June to October.

Origins
The name *Melissa* comes from the Greek word

meaning 'bee', which indicates the attractiveness of the plant to pollinating insects. Lemon balm is a native of the mountainous regions of southern Europe but is now naturalized in parts of England.

Cultivation

Lemon balm will grow freely in any soil and can be propagated by seeds, cuttings or root division in spring or autumn. The easiest method is to take stem cuttings, and their scent will be stronger if planted in moist, rich soil. Lemon balm will also thrive in window boxes or pots.

Culinary Uses

Lemon balm has a delicate flavour that allows generous use in cookery (such as in lamb or pork stuffings). It can be added to many drinks, such as fruit punches and lemon tea. Lemon balm also adds zest to fruit salads and stewed fruit, and can be used instead of lemon in jam recipes.

Other Uses

Lemon balm is claimed to induce mild perspiration, and when mixed with boiling water it makes a refreshing and soothing tea.

Lemon verbena *Lippia citriodora*

Description

Lemon verbena is a perennial shrub that grows to a height of 1–1½ feet. It has thin, pointed leaves that grow in groups of three to about 8–10 cms in length and have a very pronounced lemon fragrance. The flowers are lilac or white and appear on thin panicles at the end of summer.

Origins

This deciduous shrub was originally a native of Chile and Peru, and was introduced to this country in 1784. The plant has mainly been sought after for the scent of its essential oil, although a delicious lemony tea was frequently made from its leaves.

Cultivation

Lemon verbena is a very tender plant and will require a sunny, sheltered spot in well-drained soil. It is very reluctant to grow from seed in this country, so it is best to buy a healthy plant from a nursery or garden centre to plant in your garden. Where winters tend to be severe, lemon verbena will probably be happier growing in a pot that can be transplanted indoors at the first sign of frost.

Culinary Uses

The tangy lemon flavour makes it welcome in all kinds of drinks, fruit salads and jellies. The leaves also make a wonderful lemon tea. The leaves dry very easily whilst retaining their flavour, and it is good to have a supply over the winter.

Other Uses

The leaves have a similar action on the digestive system as mint, and will help to soothe indigestion and abdominal cramps. A cold infusion of the leaves has a wonderful tonic and astringent effect on the skin, and a few leaves added to the bath water will provide a refreshing soak. A gargle of lemon verbena water is said to cleanse the mouth and help prevent gum infection. The dried leaves are wonderful for pot-pourri.

Lovage *Levisticum officinale*

Description

Lovage has a thick, fleshy, greyish root that has a strong aromatic taste and smell. The thick, hollow erect stems grow to a height of a metre or more, with segmented leaves not unlike those of celery, to which they have a similar odour. In June and July, the plant bears umbels of yellow flowers, similar to fennel, which are followed by small yellowish-brown aromatic fruits.

Origins

Lovage is a native of the Mediterranean region, where it grows wild in the mountainous regions of the south of France, Greece and the Balkans. It is one of the old English herbs that was widely cultivated in the 14th century, particularly for use in treating jaundice and urinary problems.

Cultivation

Lovage is an easy-to-propagate perennial and should be grown either from seed or by root division. If using the root division method, plant the small plants at a distance of 30 cms apart. Seeds may be grown in the spring, but for best results they should be planted when just ripe in the summer, preferably in a sunny position. Lovage will seed freely year after year.

Culinary Uses

Lovage leaves are delightful in vegetable soups and meat casseroles and stews. The leaves and stalks can be braised as a vegetable in much the same way as celery. The leaves can also be added to salads and omelettes.

Other Uses

Lovage is not much used as a medicinal herb now, but it is said to possess diuretic properties and to stimulate the appetite.

Marigold *Calendula Officinalis*

Description

The common marigold is a familiar sight, with its pale green leaves and golden-orange flowers.

Origins

The marigold was originally a native of India and southern Europe. Hindus traditionally used it to adorn the altars of their temples.

Cultivation

Although a native of warmer climates, the marigold is perfectly hardy and easy to grow in this country. Seeds sown in April in any soil and in sunny or in partly shaded situations will germinate freely. No special care is required but regular weeding and thinning should be carried out where plants grow too closely together (i.e. less than 25 cms). They will flower in June and will continue to do so until killed by the first frost. Marigolds will increase from year to year if allowed to seed themselves.

Culinary Uses

Marigold can be used as an economical substitute for saffron. The petals (either fresh or dried) will impart a delicate flavour to a variety of cheese, rice and egg dishes, and can also be used in sponge puddings and custards. The leaves can be boiled and eaten like spinach.

Other Uses

A marigold leaf infusion makes a wonderfully soothing remedy for tired and aching feet, and is also beneficial to the skin. It is also an aid to poor circulation when taken in a tea. An ointment made from the petals gives relief from sunburn and acts as a skin tonic and softener.

Marjoram *Origanum majorana*

Description

Although there are three varieties of marjoram, sweet marjoram has the best flavour for cooking. It is a low-growing bushy plant (growing to about 20 cms in height) with small leaves and clusters of flowers that look like knots—hence its alternative name, knotted marjoram.

Origins
Sweet marjoram was originally a native of Portugal.
Cultivation
In this country, sweet marjoram is generally treated as an annual or half-hardy annual as it will not withstand winter temperatures. Generally, seeds are sown every March indoors and then transplanted outdoors after germination sometime in April. Seedlings grow slowly, and the site (preferably sunny with light soil) should be kept free of weeds. When seedlings are about 3 cm high they should be thinned out to a distance of about 15–20 cms apart.
Culinary Uses
Sweet marjoram blends particularly well with meat and vegetables such as potatoes and marrow and also in salads. The fresh leaves can also be used to make a tea or in herb vinegar. Marjoram also freezes well.
Other Uses
The dried leaves are frequently used as a pot-pourri ingredient. The essential oil of the plant is used as an external application for bruises, swellings and toothache. An infusion made from the fresh, whole plant is said to relieve nervous headaches.

Marshmallow *Althaea officinalis*

Description
The marshmallow is a pretty hardy perennial often found on marshy ground and near the coast. It can reach over a

metre in height and has attractive greyish-green, velvety leaves and pale pink flowers.

Origins

Marshmallow is native to most countries of Europe. All mallows contain an abundant mucilage, which has been credited with healing powers from the earliest times. Early Arab physicians favoured the use of the leaves as a poultice for sprains and inflammations, whilst the Roman poet Horace praised its laxative properties.

Cultivation

Marshmallow can be raised from seed in the spring or autumn but will need protection during the winter. Cuttings will also do well if planted straight into the soil, as will pieces of root, carefully divided in the autumn once the shoots have died down.
Marshmallow will thrive in almost any soil or situation but will attain greater height if the soil is moist.

Culinary Uses

Traditionally, marshmallow really was the flavouring of the popular confection of the same name, but these days the sweets are flavoured synthetically and bear little resemblance to the originals.

Other Uses

Marshmallow is mainly used as a medicinal herb in this country. An infusion of the flowers or leaves with a little honey added makes an excellent gargle for sore throats. A decoction of the roots will help chesty coughs and bronchial catarrh, whilst a poultice or ointment made from the roots will help reduce swellings and inflammations, including sunburn and other skin irritations. The root should always be peeled so that only the white fibrous part is used.

Nasturtium *Tropaeolum majus*

Description

Nasturtium is a climbing plant with stems that grow up to 1–1½ metres in length. It has striking red, yellow and gold bell-shaped flowers and attractive leaves that are shield-shaped with veins radiating out from the central stalk.

Origins

Little is known about the history of the nasturtium, although it does seem to have been native to South America. Records exist of nasturtium cultivation in England in the 16th century, although its herbal/culinary use does not seem to have been discovered until much later.

Cultivation

Nasturtiums are grown as annuals in this country. Their large seeds mean planting is easy, although they should be sown in the desired site as they do not relish transplantation. Light soil and plenty of water are required. The plants particularly dislike hot weather, especially if it is accompanied by high humidity.

Culinary Uses

Rich in iron and vitamin C, nasturtium has a peppery flavour not dissimilar to that of watercress. The young chopped leaves go well with cheese dips and sandwich spreads, and can also be added along with the flowers to a variety of salads. The seeds can be used as an alternative to capers, and should be pickled whilst young and green.

Other Uses

Nasturtium is not much used medicinally these days, but it was traditionally used to treat scurvy.

Parsley *Petroselinum crispum*

Description

There are no fewer than 37 variations of the *crispum* variety alone, but the best known and loved for culinary purposes are the common curly-leafed parsley and the French or plain-leafed parsley. The lush green foliage clumps of curly parsley usually grow to between 15 and 30 cms high.

Origins

Surprisingly, parsley is not a native of Britain—some experts say that it came from Sardinia, others that it originated in the eastern Mediterranean. However, since its introduction to this country sometime in the 16th century, it has become completely naturalized. The Greeks held parsley in high esteem, using it in crowning wreaths and to adorn the tombs of their dead.

Cultivation

Parsley requires an ordinary, well-worked soil with

full sun but perhaps a little afternoon shade. Seeds can be sown directly into the ground in April, and seedlings thinned to a distance of about 20 cms apart. The seedlings take rather a long time to germinate, sometimes as much as a month, but this can be reduced by soaking the seeds in warm water overnight prior to planting. Parsley is actually a biennial plant, but the second year's growth is rarely tender enough for eating so the plant is normally treated as an annual.

Culinary Uses

Parsley should be added to soups, sauces, eggs, salads and vegetables. It is frequently added to garlic bread and other garlic dishes in order to soften the flavour.

Other Uses

Parsley has been valued for centuries as a diuretic. Herbalists used to make a strong decoction of the root to cure kidney stones and jaundice. A traditional French remedy for swellings and boils was to pound parsley leaves in a mortar to make an ointment to apply to the affected area.

Pennyroyal *Mentha pulegium*

Description

Pennyroyal is a member of the mint family but is very different in habit from any of the others. The plant is a creeping one with weak stems about 7–15 cms high. In July and August the plant bears whorled clusters of reddish-mauve flowers.

Origins

Pennyroyal is a native of most parts of Europe and parts of Asia. It was named *pulegium* by the Romans—from the Latin *pulex*, meaning 'flea'—for its alleged powers as a flea repellent. The name pennyroyal is a corruption of the old herbalists' name 'Pulioll-royall', from the same Latin derivation.

Cultivation

Because of its vigorous growth, pennyroyal makes ideal ground cover. It grows well from seed in a loamy soil, but it is probably easier simply to divide and transplant an existing plant, which, with its thick matting of root, will quickly make new growth. It also grows well in pots and window boxes.

Culinary Uses

Pennyroyal has an extremely acrid flavour and pungent aroma and is not popular in cookery nowadays, although historically sailors would take pots of it on long voyages in order to purify drinking water. It has also been popular in the past as a tea and as a flavouring for various stuffings.

Other Uses

For centuries, pennyroyal has been credited with a variety of healing powers. The Roman writer Pliny recommended it for a multitude of sicknesses, and particularly for hanging in sick rooms. It was also claimed to cure headaches, giddiness, digestive disturbances and colds if taken in an infusion.

Peppermint *Mentha piperita*

Description

Peppermint is a handsome plant with purplish stems that reach about 60 cm in height. The pinkish-lilac flowers appear in whorled clusters in the axils of the upper leaves. It has a very distinctive aroma, which has made it popular for a multitude of uses.

Origins

The plant is native to most of Europe, although it is not commonly found growing wild in Britain. It does, however, grow wild throughout the United States, although it was probably originally a garden escape. The Greeks and Romans adorned themselves with peppermint at their feasts and flavoured their sauces and wines with it.

Cultivation

Peppermint likes a rich, moist soil in a sunny or partially shaded location. It is best to plant rooted runners about a metre apart, preferably at a distance from vulnerable plants as it tends to be fairly invasive.

Culinary Uses

Peppermint is a popular flavouring used in a wide variety of cakes, sweets and candies. Mint sauce is a traditional accompaniment to roast lamb, and mint leaves provide an interesting addition to herb vinegars. The flavour seems to blend well with many desserts and also forms the basis of some drinks, such as liqueurs and fruit punches.

Other Uses

Perhaps the best-known commercial use of mint is as a flavouring in toothpaste. The menthol constituent of the herb stimulates a cool fresh sensation in the mouth, which promotes a feeling of cleanliness, and it also has an antiseptic effect. It has also long been prized for its ability to soothe digestive disturbances, especially when taken as a tea or boiled in milk.

Purslane *Portulaca oleracea*

Description

Purslane is a herbaceous annual with a round, smooth, succulent stem that grows to about 15 cms in length. The leaves are dark green, thick and stalked, and the flowers single and yellow. The flowers bloom between June and July but tend to remain closed for most of the day, opening only for a short time towards noon.

Origins

There are two different kinds of purslane, namely the green, or garden, and the golden, both of which are distributed all over the world—in Europe, the East and West Indies, China and Japan. In ancient times it was looked upon as an 'anti-magic' herb, and when strewn round a bed was said to give protection against evil spirits.

Cultivation

Purslane seeds should be sown in early summer, or at least when any danger of frost has passed. It prefers a

sunny situation and sandy soil. Seedlings should be
thinned to a distance of 15 cms apart and kept well
watered. In warm weather they can be ready for use in
as little as 6 weeks.

Culinary Uses

Purslane's main use is as a salad herb, and it can be
pickled in vinegar to use in winter salads. The
younger shoots can be cooked and served with a
butter sauce as a vegetable. The fresh, sharp taste
also adds interest to soups, cream cheeses and
broths.

Other Uses

Traditionally, purslane was widely recommended
for a variety of complaints. Bruised and applied
to the temples and forehead, the herb was said to
remove excessive heat and headache. A distillation
of purslane was said to help toothache, sore mouths and
swollen gums, whilst external application could reduce
inflammation and swelling.

Rose *Rosa centifola*

Description

Everyone is familiar with the beautiful rose, in all its
many varieties from the wild rose to the more
complex hybrid teas and floribundas beloved of
contemporary gardeners. However, few would classify
it as a herb, although its medicinal properties have
been known for centuries.

Origins

Roses are a group of herbaceous shrubs found in temperate regions throughout both hemispheres. The birthplace of the cultivated rose was probably Persia, from whence it spread across Mesopotamia to Palestine and across Asia to Greece. The Roman writers Horace and Pliny both wrote at length on the cultivation of roses, and the word *rosa* comes from the Greek word *rodon*, meaning 'red'.

Cultivation

Wild roses are extremely hardy and will do well in almost any garden, given enough space. Otherwise, it is best to buy healthy plants from a reputable garden supplier and follow the grower's instructions.

Culinary Uses

Candied rose petals make charming cake decorations, and the petals are also popular in fruit and wine cups and punches. Rose hips (from wild roses) can be puréed for later use. A rich source of vitamin C, the purée makes a refreshingly different sauce for ice creams and desserts.

Other Uses

The essential oil of roses has been one of the most valuable ingredients in perfumery and cosmetics since ancient times. Rose petals are also popular ingredients in pot-pourri, the scent having a calming and relaxing effect. Rose-hip tea is said to have a mild diuretic and tonic effect.

Rosemary *Rosemarinus officinalis*

Description

Rosemary is an evergreen slow-growing perennial shrub that can eventually attain 1–1½ metres in height. It has short, dark green leaves that resemble pine needles and clusters of pale blue flowers, and emits a wonderful aromatic smell.

Origins

Rosemary is native to the Mediterranean countries but grows well in most temperate climes. The Greeks and Romans were well acquainted with this herb and wore sprigs of it twined through their hair in order to exploit its memory and concentration-enhancing properties. It also became an emblem of fidelity for lovers, and was used at weddings and funerals.

Cultivation

Rosemary can be propagated in a variety of ways—by seed, by cuttings and by root division. It prefers a light, rather dry soil and a sheltered situation, such as at the base of a south-facing wall. Rosemary can also be grown in a container out of doors, but will need some protection from the elements in the winter.

Culinary Uses

Traditionally, rosemary has always been teamed with roast lamb, but it also blends well with most other meats and is surprisingly good with fish and eggs. Try adding it to scones and biscuits, jellies and jams.

Rosemary also imparts an unusual flavour to fruit cups, fruit salads and wines.

Other Uses

The young tops, leaves and flowers of the plant can be made into an infusion that has been traditionally used by herbalists to alleviate the symptoms of headache, colic and colds, and also to soothe nervous complaints or stress-related disorders. It is also said to improve the condition of dark hair when added to the rinse water.

Rue *Ruta graveolens*

Description

Rue is a musky-smelling perennial cultivated for its attractive blue-green foliage and yellow blossoms. It grows to a height of around 45 cms and has a woody stem that gives it something of the character of a shrub.

Origins

The origins of this plant are in the Mediterranean, and it was introduced into Britain by the Romans, who used it in their salads. It has been called the 'herb of grace' because its bitter taste and unpleasant smell made it a symbol of sorrow and repentance. The Ancient Greeks thought that it had eyesight-improving qualities, and their artists therefore ate it to enhance their work. In England it was widely used by witch-finders and exorcists, and it was thought to offer protection from fevers and plagues. In the Middle Ages, branches of rue were used to sprinkle holy water in church.

Cultivation

Rue can be grown from seed without much difficulty. It prefers a location with full sun and does best in well-drained, sandy soil. Thin the seedlings to around 30 cm apart when they are 5 to 8 cms high and cut off their flowerheads after their first bloom. Encourage a second bloom by spreading compost around the bases of the plants. Mature rue should be cut back to half its size every spring.

Culinary Uses

Rue is not used in cooking today and should only be planted with caution as many people have a violent allergic reaction to it.

Other Uses

Rue is a very potent herb that should be used only in small doses and should never be used during pregnancy. It is most effective in treating rashes, rheumatism and cramps.

Sage *Salvia officinalis*

Description

Sage is a low-growing evergreen shrub with wiry stems that generally grows to about 30 cms in height. The leaves are greyish-green and hairy, and the flowers grow in purplish whorls. All parts of the plant have a strong, scented odour and a warm, bitter astringent taste.

Origins

Sage is native to the northern shores of the Mediterranean, but it has been cultivated for centuries in northern Europe, being hardy enough to withstand most winters. The name of the genus—*Salvia*—comes from the Latin *salvere*, 'to be saved', in reference to the curative properties of this plant.

Cultivation

Sage will grow almost anywhere in ordinary garden soil. It grows well from seed, if rather slowly, and should be planted under glass in early spring and transplanted thereafter to its permanent site. Alternatively, cuttings may be planted directly into the soil about 40–45 cms apart in late spring.

Culinary Uses

Sage is a very popular kitchen herb, perhaps appearing most famously in sage and onion stuffing. It also goes well with roast pork and duck, and can be added to most meat stews. Try chopping some fresh leaves and adding them to cheese spreads and green and tomato salads. Surprisingly, sage also goes well with fruit juices and cider and wine cups.

Other Uses

Sage has a calming effect on the digestion, which is perhaps one reason why it has become such a popular culinary herb. In infusion form, herbalists value it as an antiseptic mouthwash and throat gargle. Sage tea is said to have a cleansing and purifying effect on the blood, and to relieve

headaches. Sage is also often used as a skin tonic
and hair conditioner.

Salad burnet *Poterium sanguisorba*

Description
The salad or lesser burnet grows in clumps consisting
of flat rosettes of leaves with flower stalks that may
reach up to 30 cms in height. Both the flower stems
and the tight clusters of flowers at their end are bright
crimson in colour. The leaves are coarsely toothed and
have a flavour similar to cucumber.

Origins
The salad burnet is native to most parts of Europe and
western Asia. The name *Poterium* is derived from the
Greek *poterion,* a 'drinking cup', from the plant's
extensive use in various beverages.

Cultivation
The easiest way to grow salad burnet is to plant seeds
in ordinary or even rather poor garden soil. If initially
kept free from weeds and well watered, it will continue
to grow for years without much further attention. Existing
plants are easy to propagate, and seed scattered from the
flowerheads should germinate easily.

Culinary Uses
Salad burnet's light cucumber flavour makes it an ideal
salad herb and also a useful flavouring for drinks. It
also makes an excellent vinegar to use in salad
dressings and is pleasant in cream cheese dips.

Other Uses
An infusion of the leaves is said to have a tonic effect as a drink or as a skin tonic.

Southernwood *Artemisia abrotanum*

Description
Southernwood is a woody perennial shrub that grows to about 1 metre in height. It has finely divided greyish-green leaves that release a strong scent of lemon when bruised. It has tiny yellow flowers, but these are rarely seen in this country.

Origins
Southernwood is native to southern Europe, particularly to Spain and Italy, and was introduced into this country in 1548.

Cultivation
Southernwood is difficult to grow from seed so it is best to obtain cuttings in late summer. These should be approximately 15 cms long with a heel and should be set in sand 8 cms deep until they have rooted. The following spring, plant out the cuttings in a well-drained sheltered, sunny position. Alternatively, southernwood will also grow well in containers.

Culinary Uses
Southernwood is not widely used in cookery as it has a rather strong, bitter flavour, but it can be taken as a tonic tea if flavoured well with honey.

Other Uses

Southernwood was used traditionally as an antiseptic and a stimulant. It was claimed to have the power to reverse baldness and is still used in some commercial hair preparations. It is also reputed to possess insect- repellent and anti-parasitic properties and has been used as a cure for worms in children. The dried leaves will deter moths from laying eggs in clothing.

Summer Savory *Satureja hortensis*

Description

Summer savory is a hardy annual with erect stems about 30 cms high. It flowers in late July, having small, pale lilac and white flowers usually in groups of three.

Origins

There are about 14 species of *Satureia* native to Mediterranean regions, of which only 2, the annual summer savory and the perennial winter savoury, are generally grown in this country. Both species were noticed by the ancient Greek writer Virgil as being among the most fragrant of herbs, and he recommended that they be grown alongside beehives. Savory must have been a familiar herb in Shakespeare's day, as he mentions it in *The Winter's Tale*.

Cultivation

Summer savory is normally raised from seed in early April in shallow drills 25 to 30 cms apart. It prefers a light, rich soil. Seedlings should be thinned out to a distance of 15 cms apart. Bear in mind that the seeds can be rather slow to germinate and that the seedlings do not appreciate being transplanted.

Culinary Uses

Savory has a distinctive taste, not unlike that of marjoram, and can be added to stuffings, pork pies and sausages as a tasty seasoning. It may also be boiled with green peas, broad beans and potatoes, in the same way as mint. It is also much used in salads and as a garnish.

Other Uses

Although mainly used as a culinary herb nowadays, savory was traditionally acclaimed as a good remedy for colic and flatulence. The diluted juice was also once popular as a soothing eye-wash and a sprig of savory rubbed on bee or wasp stings will bring rapid relief.

Tansy *Tanacetum vulgare*

Description

Tansy is a hardy perennial that can grow up to a metre in height and is much admired for its fern-like leaves, 8 to 15 cms long, and its clusters of yellow, button-shaped petalless flowers. In the garden, tansy can be aggressive, its creeping roots spreading far in a short space of time and even the most severe drought unable to kill it.

Origins

Tansy is native to the British Isles and has grown here for hundreds of years. In the 16th century it was eaten in a special pudding made at Easter after six weeks' fasting because it was thought to clean out the system. It was also used as a repellent, laid on corn to keep away mice and on corpses to keep away earthworms.

Cultivation

Tansy does best in the full sun in a loamy, damp soil. Sow the seeds in spring or plant-root divisions about 30 cms apart, preferably against a wall. Always ensure that tansy has plenty of room as its roots wander.

Culinary Uses

Tea made from tansy can cause stomach upset, and as a culinary herb it is best left alone.

Other Uses

Today tansy is mainly grown for the flowerheads, which, when dried, are very popular among flower-arrangers.

Tarragon *Artemisia dracunculus*

Description

Tarragon grows to about 60 cms in height and has long, narrow, undivided leaves. It flowers in August, although the small flowers rarely open fully in this country. The roots are long and fibrous, spreading by runners.

Origins

Tarragon is a native of southern Europe.

Cultivation

As tarragon rarely produces fertile flowers in this country, the plant is best propagated by root division in March or April or by cuttings taken when growth has commenced later in the summer. It does best in warm, dry situations. In winter, the roots will need to be protected as they are susceptible to severe frost. To minimize this risk, tarragon is best planted in rather poor, dry soil. It also does well in containers.

Culinary Uses

Tarragon has a multitude of culinary uses. It can be added to salads of many kinds, and tarragon vinegar— made by steeping the fresh leaves in white wine vinegar—is a popular ingredient for French dressing. Tarragon goes well with roast meat as well as many poultry and fish dishes.

Other Uses

Tarragon has always enjoyed greater popularity as a culinary rather than a medicinal herb. However, it was traditionally used as a remedy for the bites and stings of venomous beasts and mad dogs.

Thyme *Thymus vulgaris*

Description

Garden thyme is a creeping perennial that reaches a maximum height of 45 cms. It has small greenish-grey elliptical leaves and tiny whorls of mauve flowers that last for about a month in the summer.

Origins

The garden thyme is an 'improved' cultivated form of the wild thyme found in the mountains of Spain and other countries bordering the Mediterranean, as well as in parts of Asia, Algeria and Tunisia. It is also a near relation of our own wild thyme, which has broader leaves and a weaker aroma than garden thyme. The name thyme was given to the plant by the Greeks as a derivation of a word meaning 'to fumigate', perhaps signifying its cleansing properties. It is much loved by bees, and the honey that is produced near Athens is said to owe its wonderful flavour to the wild thyme growing locally in abundance.

Cultivation

Thyme can be raised from seed in spring in the growing position and then thinned to 30 cms apart. Alternatively, an established plant may be divided and transplanted. In either case, it prefers a light, well-drained soil and a sunny position.

Culinary Uses

Thyme has a powerful flavour and should be used sparingly in cooking unless a taste for it has been established. It adds a delicious flavour to a multitude of meats, stews, fish and herb sauces. It also compliments many side vegetables, such as carrots and potatoes.

Other Uses

Infusion of thyme is said to cure sore throats and

catarrh if given several times daily. In an ointment, thyme will relieve swellings and warts, and is said to promote a clear complexion. A cup of hot tea taken late at night will often soothe away insomnia.

Valerian *Valeriana officinalis*

Description
Valerian grows to a height of about 1–1½ metres. The leaves are made up of a series of lance-shaped segments more or less opposite each other. In mid-summer, clusters of small pale pink flowers appear. The whole plant has a rather fetid smell, which intensifies when bruised.

Origins
The genus comprises about 150 species, which are widely distributed in temperate parts of the world. Two of the species—*Valeriana officinalis* and *Valeriana dioca*—are indigenous in Britain. Today it has no culinary use, but it was used by the Anglo-Saxons as a salad herb and the Elizabethans enjoyed it in their broth. The odour of valerian is especially attractive to rats and the Pied Piper of Hamelin is said to have used it as bait.

Cultivation
Valerian is a hardy perennial that grows well in most soils but prefers a rich, moist loam and a sunny position. Valerian can be grown from seed, preferably in pots under glass initially. The seeds are very slow to

germinate, but thereafter seedlings should be planted out to a distance of 60 cms apart. It is much easier, however, to propagate valerian by root division at the end of summer.

Culinary Uses
Valerian is not used in cookery.

Other Uses
The root is the part of the plant that has been valued for centuries in herbal medicine. It seems to promote a calming effect on the nerves, and was traditionally used to allay pain and promote sleep. However, care should be taken with large doses of valerian tea as too much can cause headache and stupor. The root has also been used in an ointment to treat skin sores and other conditions.

Watercress *Nasturtium officinale*

Description
Watercress is a hardy perennial plant that grows in abundance near springs and running water. It has shiny, rounded leaves on fleshy stems that grow to a height of about 30 cms. The flowers are tiny and white and are followed by long seed pods.

Origins
Watercress is native to most parts of Europe.

Cultivation
Watercress is best grown in 10 cms of running water with a base of 7 cms of sandy soil. Grow the seeds in boxes,

then plant out the seedlings at a distance of 15 cms apart.

Culinary Uses
Watercress is rich in iron and vitamin C, and it is a popular salad ingredient and garnish.

Other Uses
Watercress was used historically to ward off scurvy and in the treatment of tuberculosis. Infusions made from the young shoots are said to be beneficial in rheumatism, digestive disturbances and catarrh, but should not be taken over extended periods of time.

Yarrow *Achillea millefolium*

Description
Yarrow has a rough, angular stem and dark, feathery leaves arranged alternately the length of the stem. It has large, flat-topped clusters of white or pale lilac flowers that bloom from June to September. The plant generally reaches a height of around 60 cms.

Origins
Yarrow is native to Britain and grows freely everywhere.

Cultivation
Yarrow spreads by its roots and by seeding freely, and it is rarely admitted to gardens in this country as it is generally regarded as a troublesome weed. It will thrive in the poorest of soils and conditions, and must be kept in check if it is not to strangle other plants.

Culinary Uses
Both flowers and leaves have a bitter, astringent and pungent flavour, and are not generally favoured in cookery.

Other Uses
Yarrow infusion is often used as a skin tonic and to bring relief to sufferers of measles, chicken pox and other skin eruptions. Yarrow tea acts as a mild diuretic and can bring relief in pre-menstrual tension and cramp. A stronger yarrow tea is a good remedy for severe cold symptoms and can help to reduce fever. Traditionally, it was used on flesh wounds as it was credited with the promotion of the rapid formation of scar tissue. The fresh leaves are reputed to cure toothache when chewed.